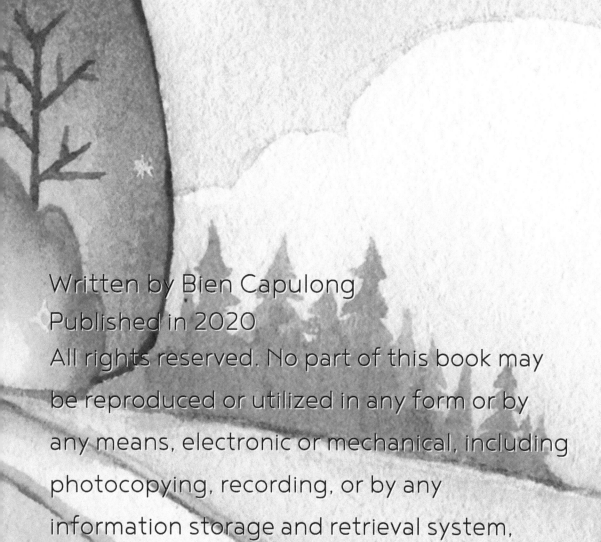

This book belongs to

_____

and I want to share it with

_____

One day, the world will get to see,

the future that lies in front of me.

One day,
    the grey skies will fade,

as your beauty is on parade.

One day, the brightest stars will fall,

for you will outshine them all.

One day, you will light the way,

and lead the others to a brighter day.

One day, your courage will be undeterred,

by fears, doubts and thoughtless words.

And one day,
  you will see what I see,

that you can be whoever you want to be.

I know you'll be honest, kind and wise,

for I already see this in your eyes.

# But for now, these hands will protect you,

from everything that makes you feel blue.

# F

or now, these arms will embrace

you everyday,

until you grow and conquer the world...

one day.

CPSIA information can be obtained
at www.ICGtesting.com
Printed in the USA
LVHW070403100221
678810LV00022B/378